LUCIE ATTWELL TINIES' BOOK OF PRAYERS

MABEL LUCIE ATTWELL

First published 1967
Reprinted 1982, 1983, 1984, 1985
Published by Deans International Publishing
52-54 Southwark Street, London SE1 1UA
A division of The Hamlyn Publishing Group Limited
London · New York · Sydney · Toronto

Illustrations Copyright © Mabel Lucie Attwell 1967

ISBN 0 603 08568 7

Printed and bound in Great Britain by
Purnell and Sons (Book Production) Ltd., Paulton, Bristol.
Member of BPCC plc

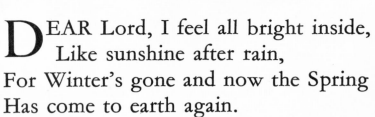

DEAR Lord, I feel all bright inside,
   Like sunshine after rain,
For Winter's gone and now the Spring
Has come to earth again.

A.G.

FATHER, we thank Thee
        for this day
That we have spent in happy play;
We thank Thee for the fun we've had,
With nothing there to make us sad.

Father, we thank Thee for each hour,
For every bird and plant and flower,
For apple-tart and ginger-cake,
The kind that mothers always make.

Father, we thank Thee for ice-cream,
For lots of sweets: now, may we dream
That we are living in a land
Where ALL have these things from Thy
        hand?
                                        A.G.

THERE is a carpet soft and green
That everyone on earth has seen;
It may be rough or smooth as glass,
This God's own carpet made of grass.

And on this carpet, gay and free,
We dance our thanks, dear Lord, to Thee,
And say, with all our hearts, we know
The world is good while grass
    can grow.   A.G.

UNDER this umbrella,
  We watch the raindrops fall,
And, because You guard us,
We can't be hurt at all.

So, dear God, we thank Thee,
For all those raindrops bring
Fresh water for the earth
To help each growing thing. A.G.

GOD bless the birds that sweetly sing,
On branch of tree or on the wing;
May robin, thrush, or lark on high
Bring to us music from the sky.

For all the birds, from far or near,
Are God's own choir that we can hear;
So help us, Lord, to listen to
This music coming straight from You.

A.G.

OUR Father, who art in Heaven,
  Hallowed be Thy name,
Thy Kingdom come,
Thy will be done—
In earth as it is in Heaven.
Give us this day our daily bread,
And forgive us our trespasses,
As we forgive them that trespass
  against us.
And lead us not into temptation;
But deliver us from evil.
For Thine is the Kingdom,
The Power and the Glory,
For ever and ever.

                              Amen

APPLES, rosy cheeked and sweet,
Come from God for us to eat;
Make us content with all we find
Placed on earth by Him so kind;
A God of splendour and of right,
Almighty there in Heaven's sight.

A.G.

AS here I lay me down to sleep,
I pray Thee, God, my soul to keep;
And in the morning, when I wake,
Please make me good for Jesus' sake.

OUR thanks, dear God,
we give to You,
For everything so fresh
and new;
The flowers that grow,
the creatures small,
We know that You have
made them all.

The rabbits, deer and
  puppies too,
Each owes its little life to
  You;
So guard and keep them
  safe from harm,
In wood or field or glade
  or farm.

A.G.

BECAUSE, dear Lord, we've had such fun,
    We could not leave out anyone;
And so our dolls and toys and we
Kneel down to say these prayers to Thee.

We kneel because we know we ought
To thank You for the day You brought,
And even Teddy knows that he
Must give his thanks, dear God, to Thee.

But just before we climb in bed,
Our prayers and thanks to Thee all said,
Please may we ask just one more thing:
Another day like this You'll bring!

A.G.

THIS world can give such happiness,
  If people will be kind,
And give you all the sort of home
That I've been glad to find.

So, Jesus, give a happy home
To all the girls and boys,
Please give them warmth and tenderness,
And lots of lovely toys.

Then they will thank Thee in their prayers
For lots of things to love;
But, most of all, they'll love Thee, Lord,
In Heaven up above.

A.G.

HELP make this world a bright place
    where
Each life can make a pattern fair,
And where we all can do our best
To bring contentment, peace, and rest.

Please teach us, Lord, each girl and boy,
To do our work with pride and joy.
So that, when each one's task is done,
We'll say: "Dear God, it's been such fun."

A.G.

O gentle Jesus, once so small,
　　We pray that Thou wilt help
　　　　us all
To be so tender and so kind
To every creature we may find;
Protect and watch and guard, we pray,
The furry creatures every day.
Then when the night is cold and dark,
O gentle Jesus, wilt Thou mark
Each nest and burrow they have found,
In tree, or in the frosty ground,
And let Thy angels guard each one
Till daytime brings the warming sun.

A.G.

O GOD, make every prayer I pray
    A bright and shining star,
Until a stardust path is made
To reach You where You are.

A.G.

DEAR Jesus, through the daylight hours
Please help us tend the scented
flowers,
To bring them water so that they
Can look so bright and sweet and gay;
And may the little birds all find
Seeds of every sort and kind.

A.G.

LORD, give all people love at last,
 That wars and strife might cease;
And all the troubles of the past
Give way to lasting peace.

A.G.

W HEN one more day is left behind,
We pray that we might always find
A book to teach us how to say:
"We thank Thee, Lord, for this good day.

"We thank Thee, Lord, for the joy and fun,
We thank Thee for the golden sun,
We thank Thee for the food we eat,
And all the good friends that we meet."

A.G.

NOW the day has ended,
    And the shadows creep,
Bless me till tomorrow,
Keep me safe in sleep.

Let my dreams be peaceful,
Like angels' tales of love,
Each a gentle message
From Thy throne above.

Keep me, Lord, till morning,
And, when I awake,
Make me good and kindly
Just for Jesus' sake.

A.G.